Whole Language Series
Living Things

written by Janie Mellecker Uhlig and Karri Jesson Ham
illustrated by Priscilla Burris

JANIE MELLECKER UHLIG received a Bachelor of Arts degree and a Master of Arts degree from the University of Northern Colorado. She is an experienced elementary and special education teacher and has taught evening classes for the University of Northern Colorado. She has in-serviced several school districts in the use of learning centers and classroom management. Janie Uhlig is the co-author of a learning centers idea kit and other educational materials.

KARRI JESSON HAM received a Bachelor of Arts degree in elementary education and a Master of Arts degree in reading from the University of Northern Colorado. She is an experienced elementary teacher and has taught several in-services in northern Colorado. She is the author of other educational materials.

PRISCILLA BURRIS received an Associate of Arts degree in Creative Design from the Fashion Institute of Design and Merchandising in Los Angeles. As a free-lance artist of child-related artwork, she has been drawing since she was one year old. Priscilla lives in Southern California.

Copyright 1989 by **THE MONKEY SISTERS, INC.**
22971 Via Cruz
Laguna Niguel, CA 92677

ISBN 0-933606-71-0

The Writing Process

Pre-Writing: As a motivation to beginning any written work, use the introductory activity for each unit.

As a quick evaluation of the students' prior knowledge and as a teacher-guide for the gathering of resources and the selection of activities, brainstorm with your class using a question such as, "Tell me everything you know about. . . ." Record all responses and display the list.

Using the ideas gathered, collect as many resources as possible including fiction and non-fiction reading materials, realia, guest speakers, local exhibits or places to visit, etc. Based on these resources, students will begin the unit through teacher and student reading and sharing. The activities will foster the writing process.

Writing the Rough Draft: Writing suggestions to compliment the topic are included in each unit. Encourage writing through such questions as, "What do you already know?" and "What else do you want to know?"

Revising the Writing: Encourage partner-revising. Authors need audiences. The writer can read the rough draft and evaluate the listener's reactions through questions such as:

- What was my topic?
- Name three important things I wrote about my topic.
- What part was the most interesting?
- What part was confusing?
- What do you think I left out about my topic?

By receiving the listener's reactions, the writer can make decisions about what is strong in the written work and what information is weak, or perhaps, missing. Students should vary their audiences and the opportunities for revision help . . . classmates, teachers, students from other classes, parents, aides, etc.

Editing for Mechanics: Some natural editing is accomplished through the process of the student reading aloud during the revision stage. One of the most effective methods of editing one's own work is to simply read aloud to oneself.

Students with strengths in specific mechanical skills (capitalization, punctuation, spelling) can offer help to one another. The teacher should be considered the 'final editor!'

The Final Work: Ideas for final drafts are included with each unit. These can be shared in a variety of ways— library displays, sharing with another class, bulletin board displays, class booklets distributed to student's homes, etc. It is fun to include a sheet of paper encouraging comments from the reader to the writer.

Living Things

Introduction

The **Whole Language Series** consists of the following three titles and units:

Everyday Things	Living Things	People and Places
Wheels	Cattle	Helen Keller
Water	Spiders	Walt Disney
Windows	Penguins	Hans Christian Andersen
Paper	Dolphins	The Rocky Mountains
Popcorn	Wildflowers	New York City
Parties	Trees	The Great Lakes

Each of the six units contains an outline/guide sheet which gives an introduction and overview of the unit. For each page of activity, the guide sheet lists the curriculum area/skill, type of activity and page number. A suggested culminating activity is given.

As each unit's contents are varied, different curriculum areas will be focused upon based on the topic. In each one, however, a variety of subject is covered. We encourage these ideas to be expanded upon or eliminated based on the grade level and ability of your class.

Due to the variety of material presented, we suggest the following be considered with these grade levels:

Grades 2-3: Activities may be more large group/class oriented.

Grades 3-4: Activities may be more small group/individually oriented.

Grades 4-5: Activities are more individually oriented. Some lessons will still lend themselves to class projects.

Round out these teaching units by setting up a center in your classroom with library books, photographs, charts, samples and other items of interest to provide motivation to the unit. Show filmstrips, videos or films of the topic being studied and explore other centers of interest outside the classroom to enhance the study further.

TABLE OF CONTENTS

Cattle

INTRODUCTION: Have the class do a semantic mapping activity on a piece of butcher paper. Students will generate ideas and subtopics to study and you will gain an understanding of the students' prior knowledge. Hang the map in the room for the duration of the unit. An example of a semantic map on whales is shown here.

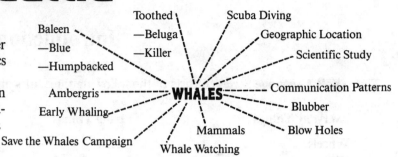

CURRICULUM AREA/SKILLS:	ACTIVITY/TITLE	PAGE NO.

Oral reading; writing tall tales — "Tall Tale Time" — No activity page
Read *Paul Bunyan and His Blue Ox* aloud and discuss the characteristic of exaggeration. Continue this format with other tall tales, making poster lists of exaggerations to display as resources for the children to use in their writing. Discuss which elements of a story (characters, setting, etc.) lend themselves to exaggeration. Students write their own tall tales using cattle-related words and terms on long (tall) pieces of paper.

Language arts; poetry — "Mooo-ving Limericks" — 2
Read several examples of limericks and discuss the pattern of rhyme and the humor. The 1st, 2nd and 5th lines rhyme with each other and the 3rd and 4th lines, which are shorter, form a rhyming couplet. Students work together on a class limerick and also write their own.

Bulletin board — "Beefy Bulletin Boards" — 3
Display limericks and tall tales using the suggested ideas and layouts or by designing your own.

Language arts; creative writing — "Amazing Advertising" — 4-5
Through introduction and exposure to various techniques of persuasion, students will become aware of the power behind advertising and have an opportunity to use their own writing skills to influence an audience.

Descriptive writing — "Compare the Cattle" — 6
Students do research to learn the various breeds of dairy and beef cattle and complete a pictorial page describing two of each type.

Science — "Digestive Systems are Different" — 7
Students do research to find out about the unique digestive systems of cattle. Present the material to younger students and work together to complete a diagram and discuss the differences between humans and cattle.

Social studies; mapping — "Where's the Beef?" — 8
Mapping skills are reinforced through an activity of locating cattle-producing states and provinces. An activity map page is provided.

Math — "Holy Cow!" — 9
Graphing skills are reinforced through an analysis of beef cattle prices and an activity in which the students collect their own data for graphing.

Art — "Dairy Designs" — 10
As an art activity related to both the study of cattle and advertising, students design a milk carton for a dairy company.

CULMINATION: As an extension to the advertising unit, students present their campaign to other classes with videotapes or by visiting other rooms. Children should also be given an opportunity to share their limericks and tall tales.

Living Things © THE MONKEY SISTERS, INC.

Mooo-ving Limericks

There once was a boy named Pete
Who had enormous, gargantuan feet,
    He saved money on fees
    For renting his skis
Even though he came down on his seat.

Class Limerick

(a) _____

(a) _____

    (b) _____

    (b) _____

(a) _____

Pre-writing Jot List: Make a list of words which rhyme with your topic. List funny things associated with your topic.

Topic: _____

Rhyming Words	Funny Ideas
_____	_____
_____	_____
_____	_____
_____	_____
_____	_____

Beefy Bulletin Boards

Amazing Advertising

Introduce the study of advertising techniques by presenting teams of 4-5 students with current ad slogans for identification of a product being sold. The activity will help to impress upon the children the power behind advertising.

Examples: **Built for the Human Race** (Nissan)
The Health Kick (milk)

Brainstorm situations where and when advertising is used. Introduce the terms "persuade-persuasion." Discuss—and have available—magazine cut outs or videotaped examples of commonly used techniques. Introduce the name and desired effect for various techniques.

Examples of techniques:
Bandwagon: Everyone's doing it.
Transfer: Using a positive symbol to cover one's goals.
Plain Folks: "I'm one of you, so you can trust what I tell you."
Testimonial: Using someone famous to endorse a cause or product.
Repetition: Using the person or product name over and over.

• Encourage the students to collect TV and magazine ads to share in class. Choose a product of interest to your students and work together to design an ad following one or a combination of techniques.

• Assign teams of children to design an advertising campaign to persuade the public to increase beef consumption or to discourage the eating of red meat. This activity could stimulate making surveys of family preferences, the study of fact vs. opinion, and even debate.

• Arrange for classroom visits from nutritionists, representatives of a beef company or feed lot, an advertising expert, etc.

• The children might enjoy combining writing, acting, taping, and special art work in the completion of the campaign. It may be helpful to divide the class into four groups—each group focusing on one specific media—for a product and slogan that has been voted on by the students.

Advertising Campaign Worksheet

Product:

Slogan:

Television: Briefly describe your advertisement, including the technique(s) used, the time required, props, etc. The ad will be performed for the class.

Product: _____

Technique(s): _____

Props: _____

Time required: _____

Radio: Include an explanation of the technique, sound effects used, and submit dialogue copy. The ad will be taped for presentation to the class.

Product: _____

Technique(s): _____

Sound equipment: _____

Dialogue copy: Check if ready ☐

Magazine or Newspaper Insert: The advertisement and the persuasion technique should be explained. Your ad should be in full color and ready for publication.

Product: _____

Magazine: ☐ Newspaper ☐

Technique(s): _____

Color copy: Check if ready ☐

Billboard or flyer: An explanation of the technique should accompany the final product. The finished billboard should be in miniature (poster size.)

Product: _____

Billboard: ☐ Flyer: ☐

Technique(s): _____

Color copy: Check if ready ☐

Compare the Cattle

Use encyclopedias and library books to copy photographs of two breeds of beef cattle and two breeds of dairy cattle. You may also cut photographs from brochures. Below each one, label the breed and describe its appearance.

Breed: _____

Beef: ☐   Dairy ☐

Description: _____

_____

_____

Breed: _____

Beef: ☐   Dairy ☐

Description: _____

_____

_____

Breed: _____

Beef: ☐   Dairy ☐

Description _____

_____

_____

Breed: _____

Beef: ☐   Dairy ☐

Description _____

_____

_____

Digestive Systems are Different

1. Have you ever wondered what the term "the cow was chewing its cud" really means? Research the digestive system of a cow and explain what it means when a cow is chewing its cud.

_____

_____

_____

_____

2. Draw a diagram of a cow's stomach and label the four different sections.

3. How is a cow's digestive system different from a person's digestive system?

_____

_____

_____

_____

Living Things © THE MONKEY SISTERS, INC.

Where's the Beef?

1. Label the states on the map.
2. Use a light blue crayon or pencil to shade the five states that produce the most beef cattle.
3. Use a pink crayon or pencil to shade the top five dairy states.

Holy Cow!

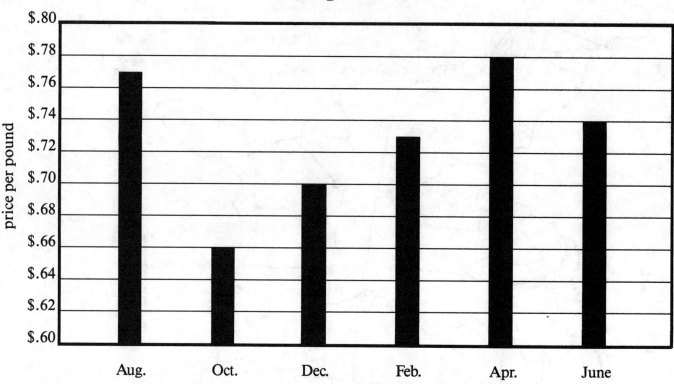

Use the bar graph to answer the following questions:

1. As a cattle farmer, how much would you receive per pound if you sold cattle in

   August? _____

2. According to the graph, in which month would you receive the most money per

   pound? _____

3. How much per pound would you receive if you sold cattle in June? _____

4. What are the advantages of recording information on a graph? List three reasons:

   _____

   _____

- -

Do a class survey to see which of the following meats are the most popular.
Tally the results.

beef _____   pork _____   lamb _____

chicken_____   fish _____   turkey _____

After you have completed the survey, make a graph to record the results.

Dairy Designs

A dairy company has asked you to create a design for a new milk carton. Using crayons, colored pencils or markers, create an original milk carton for the company. Look at information on existing milk cartons to see what needs to be included. Complete your project by covering a milk carton with your design.

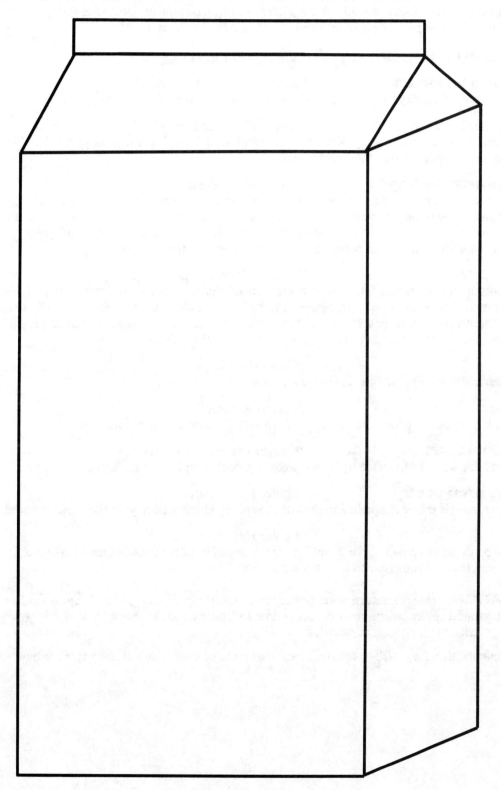

SPIDERS

INTRODUCTION: As a springboard for discussion, ask students what they already know about spiders as well as what facts they would like to learn about them. Display the list.

Using a variety of books about spiders, introduce or reinforce the concept of fiction and non-fiction. To stimulate interest and provide a good model, read aloud selections from both types of books. Each student should then select a book to read independently about spiders—fiction or non-fiction. After independent reading, students are ready to complete the activity sheet, *"Spiders: Real or Imaginary."*

CULMINATION: Set up an information center about spiders in the classroom. Display students' completed written work around spider bulletin board. Allow time for students to share booklets with a variety of audiences—parents, other classes, principal, etc.

For older students, they may wish to dramatize selected parts of *Charlotte's Web* by E. B. White.

Living Things © THE MONKEY SISTERS, INC.

SPIDERS: REAL OR IMAGINARY

Directions: Select a fiction or non-fiction book and complete one of the activities below.

Non-Fiction: *Spiders have eight legs.* From your reading, write eight more facts about spiders.

1. _____

2. _____

3. _____

4. _____

5. _____

6. _____

7. _____

8. _____

Fiction

1. Tell about the spider in the story you read.

_____

_____

_____

2. Describe the setting of the story you read.

_____

_____

_____

3. Retell your favorite part of the story.

_____

_____

_____

SPIDER CINQUAIN POETRY

The cinquain is a form of poetry which consists of five lines.

Line 1—one word of two syllables introducing the subject
Line 2—two words or four syllables describing the subject
Line 3—three words or six syllables showing action
Line 4—four words or eight syllables expressing a feeling or observation about the
      subject
Line 5—one word of two syllables renaming or describing the subject

Example:

Rainbows
Blazing colors
Arching and shimmering
Colorful spectrum in the sky
Beauty

Class poem: _____

_____

_____

_____

_____

On your own: _____

_____

_____

_____

_____

     Living Things © THE MONKEY SISTERS, INC.

WRITE-A-SPIDER-STORY

Title: _____

_____

_____

_____

_____

_____

_____

_____

_____

_____

_____

_____

_____

_____

_____

_____

_____

_____

_____

_____

SPIDER OBSERVATIONS

Directions: Choose any three different spiders to observe from your class collection. Fill in the chart below based on what you observe.

	Draw a diagram and label body parts. Use a reference book to help you.	Describe any special features.	Identify the spider through research.
Spider #____			
Spider #____			
Spider #____			

1. What conclusions can you make from your observations of the three spiders?

_____

_____

_____

2. Compare and contrast the three spiders.

_____

_____

_____

CREATE-A-WEB

Directions: Using various geometric shapes, create your own, original spider web. You might want to try using different sizes of squares, circles, triangles, rectangles, etc. When you are finished, draw a spider to go on your web.

1. What shapes did you use?

_____

_____

2. Do you have any *parallel* lines? Outline each set with a red crayon.

3. Do you have any *perpendicular* lines? Outline them with a blue crayon.

4. Do you have any *right angles*? Outline them with a yellow crayon.

5. Do you have any *acute angles*? Outline them with an orange crayon.

6. Do you have any *obtuse angles*? Outline them with a purple crayon.

Name _____

SPIDER STUMPERS

Directions: Using reference materials and/or library books, look up the answers to the following questions.

1. How are spiders helpful to people?

_____

_____

2. What is the main difference between spiders and insects?

_____

_____

3. What are two facts about a spider's eyes?

_____

_____

4. Why is the spider's silky web so important to a spider?

_____

_____

5. What is the difference between a web-spinning spider and a hunting spider?

_____

_____

6. What kinds of spiders are common in your area?

_____

_____

7. What are four kinds of poisonous spiders?

_____

_____

8. Draw a diagram of a spider and label the following parts: eyes, mouth, chelicerae, pedipalpi, abdomen.

_____

_____

CAUGHT IN A WEB OF POETRY

Suggested Activities:

• Display students' cinquain poems using the sample pattern or originals from the students' own designs.

• Try this art activity to appreciate the beauty of the web while comparing web structures: Use a bright colored spray paint to coat a web, and then carefully lift the web with a sheet of black construction paper while the paint is still wet. The color-coated web will stick to the paper, creating a lovely illustration of the structure of the web. These can be used with comparison questions in discussions and as backdrops for numerous types of writing activities.

• Students can design their own webs using colored-paper backgrounds with webs made of yarn, fishing line or string. Attach using white glue. Stories and reports on real or imaginary spiders can compliment the webs.

SPIDER POETRY PATTERN

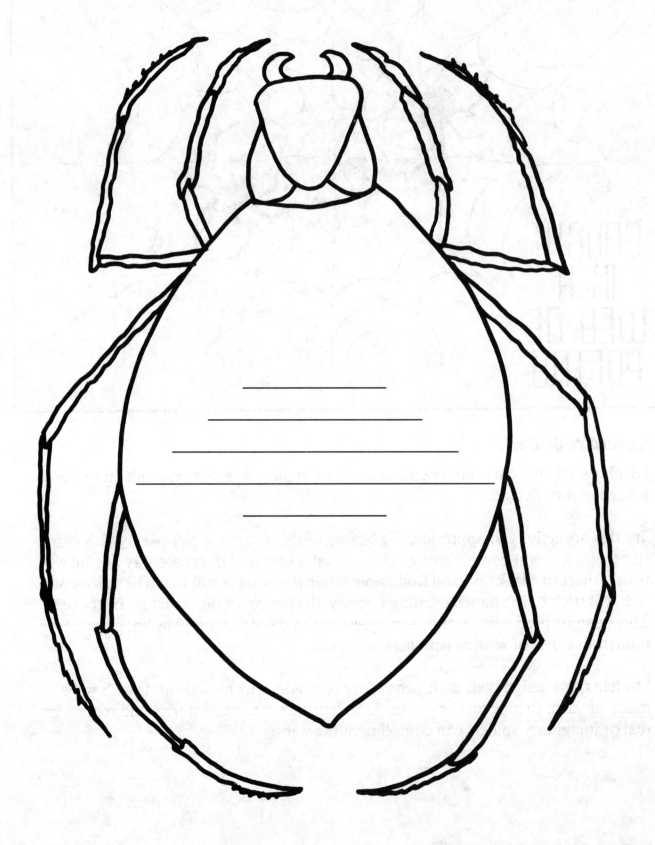

SPIDER HATS—SPIDER MOBILES

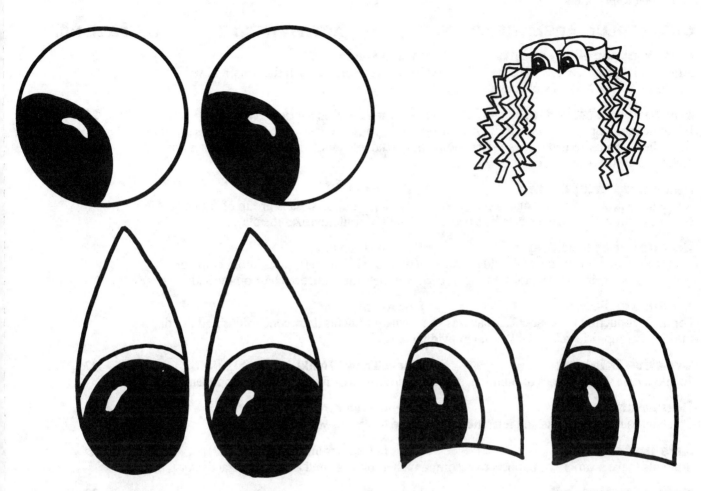

Materials: Black construction paper; 9 strips each of 2″ x 24″ (5cm x 60cm); scissors, glue or stapler.

Directions:

- Duplicate eye patterns above and distribute one to each student.
- Cut out one set of eyes and glue to hat band strip.
- Accordion fold eight strips for legs.
- Attach legs to hat band using a stapler or glue.
- For mobile, attach string to opposite sides of hat band, tie at top and hang around room.

Note: Older students (grades 3 and up) may enjoy making the hats and presenting them to a class of kindergarteners, first or second graders. If you do this, leave hat bands open and have your students fit these on the children when presented. Be sure to make enough hats for the class you present them too!

Penguins

INTRODUCTION: Read *Mr. Popper's Penguin's,* by Richard and Florence Atwater to your students. Discuss the factual information found in the story. Bring magazine articles and books about penguins and have students read them. View films and filmstrips to see how they move. Have each student tell one interesting fact pertaining to penguins.

CURRICULUM AREA/SKILLS:	ACTIVITY/TITLE	PAGE NO.

CULMINATION: Have a penguin party! Brainstorm with the class for theme-related activities and food: ice cream bars, frozen yogurt, oreo cookies, black and white decorations, dressing in black and white only for the party, etc. For entertainment, students may wish to have a penguin trivia game, invite other classes to see their puppet plays and puppet parade. If easily accessible, arrange for the class to visit penguins at the local zoo.

Make A Story Cube

Write a sentence on each of the six sides of the cube pattern describing an event in the story of *Mr. Popper's Penguins* by Richard and Florence Atwater. Make an illustration to accompany each sentence. When you are finished, cut out the pattern and fold it into a cube. Use tape or glue to keep it in place.

Patterned Penguin Stories

Read a variety of *Choose Your Own Adventure* stories (Bantam Books) to the children. Note the element of decision making at critical points in the plot and the way the author makes the reader the continual main character. Using one of the books as a model, introduce the following concrete pattern for writing a group story.

• Class as a whole and divide as it develops *or* 4-6 students to begin.

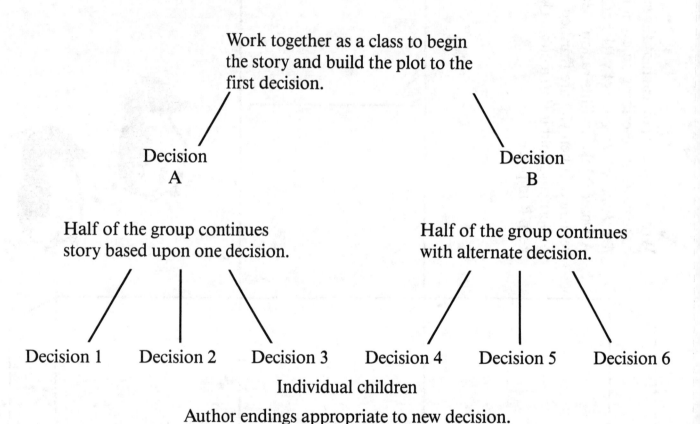

Work together as a class to begin the story and build the plot to the first decision.

Decision A

Decision B

Half of the group continues story based upon one decision.

Half of the group continues with alternate decision.

Decision 1 Decision 2 Decision 3 Decision 4 Decision 5 Decision 6

Individual children

Author endings appropriate to new decision.

At each new decision point, the author must provide the reader with a page to turn to which continues the plot based upon the reader's decision. The page numbering must be done at the end of the total writing activity so as to coincide with the number of pages required to develop any given plot direction.

Assign the class to write a patterned adventure story related to the penguin unit of study—perhaps a setting on the continent of Antarctica, employing the class learnings of the unique features of the geography and climate; or a story with main characters being scientists, or even penguins. . . .

A Penguin Play

Even though the book, *Mr. Popper's Penguins* is a humorous fictional story, it provides factual information about penguins. Working in groups of 4-6 students, write an original play or skit about penguins which could be acted out using finger puppets. Your play should incorporate information about penguins that you have learned during the course of this unit. When you have finished writing your play, assign parts, create puppets (see page 29) and practice acting it out. Complete the evaluation below and turn it in before presenting your play.

Title: _____

Group Members: _____   _____

_____   _____

_____   _____

Characters in Play: _____

_____

_____

Setting: _____

_____

A problem the character/characters face: _____

_____

_____

Brief summary of play: _____

_____

_____

_____

_____

What will your audience learn about penguins from watching your play?

_____

_____

_____

_____

Emperor Penguins

Emperor penguins have very interesting nesting habits. Read about emperor penguins and complete the chart below recording the sequence of events involved in their nesting process.

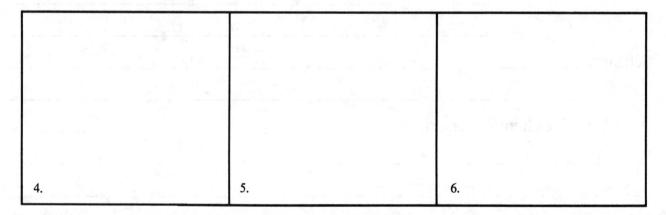

1.	2.	3.

A female penguin comes in from the ocean and lays an egg in her rookery.

4.	5.	6.

7.	8.	9.

In about six months, the baby penguins can care for themselves. The penguins then return to the ocean.

Discover My Land

Present the following factual statements orally, in the prescribed order. Each fact has a point value which decreases as additional information is presented. The winner(s) are awarded the value at the point at which the correct identification is made. (Assign teams to make guesses or have students guess independently.) Have a world map visible for the students.

Directions: Students number their papers from 1-10. Divide class into groups of 4-6 or work individually to guess the geographical location from the clues read. Students should not guess aloud, but after each fact, write their guess down on their paper. When each new clue is given, they may revise their guess.

10 points	1. It is a large body of land.	_____
9 points	2. It is located in the southern hemisphere.	_____
8 points	3. It is the sight of many scientific experiments.	_____
7 points	4. It is almost 5,100,000 square miles, larger than the United States and Mexico combined.	_____
6 points	5. Many different countries claim to own this land.	_____
5 points	6. It is 90% covered with ice and snow.	_____
4 points	7. It is the coldest spot on earth, with temperatures sometimes dropping to − 126 °F.	_____
3 points	8. It is the sight of the South Pole.	_____
2 points	9. It is home to several species of marine birds, including the penguin.	_____
1 point	10. It is the continent of Antarctica.	_____

Think! Think! Think!

Directions: Read the following five thinking activities carefully. Select three of the five activities to complete. Attach your finished work to this page. Circle the numbers of the three activities you have selected.

1. **Fluent Thinking:** List as many words as you can to describe a penguin. However, you must list a minimum of 10 words.

2. **Flexible Thinking:** What would happen if . . .
    —the Antarctic ice melted?
    —you received a penguin to care for?

3. **Original Thinking:** Prepare a biographical sketch of the life of an Antarctic research scientist, *or* design a cartoon to star a penguin.

4. **Elaborative Thinking:** Write a new ending to the story of *Mr. Popper's Penguins.*

5. **Evaluative Thinking:** Prepare a speech on the need for laws to protect animals.

Penguin Stumpers

1. What is a penguin's nest called?

   _____

   _____

   _____

2. How do the parent penguins feed the baby birds?

   _____

   _____

   _____

3. Pretend that you have been asked to design an area for penguins at a zoo. Explain what you would include in the area to make the penguins comfortable.

   _____

   _____

   _____

4. How is a penguin's body adapted to life in the sea and also from cold temperatures?

   _____

   _____

   _____

5. What does it mean when a penguin is *moulting*?

   _____

   _____

   _____

6. Penguins look like they are dressed in tuxedos. Why is their body coloring important to their survival?

   _____

   _____

   _____

Penguin Puppets

A variety of penguin puppets may be constructed using materials from school and home. Have children create balloon puppets, stick puppets, finger puppets, paper bag puppets, paper plate puppets, etc. and have a penguin puppet parade.

Balloon Puppets: *Materials:* white balloons, permanent markers, orange tagboard or construction paper
Directions: Inflate the white balloons to a variety of sizes. Use the colored markers to decorate the balloon to resemble a penguin. Using the pattern, make orange feet to support the penguin. Insert balloon tie in slit in foot pattern.

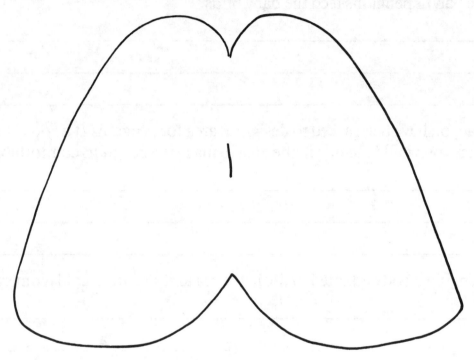

Note: Plastic "eggs" can also be decorated using the same idea.

The following illustrations show the variety of puppets using readily available materials. Set up a center where the children may experiment with these and perhaps even create something new.

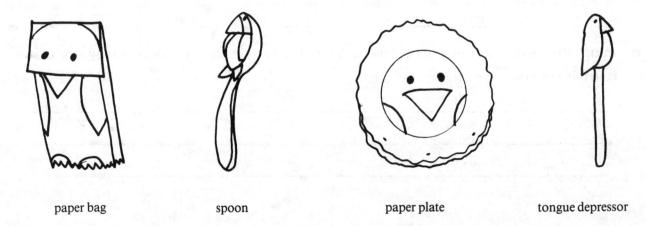

paper bag   spoon   paper plate   tongue depressor

Make-A-Map

Directions: Create a *relief map* of Antarctica. Show landforms with mountain features as well as surrounding bodies of water. Label these with small flags attached to toothpicks and insert in appropriate places. Use heavy corrugated board or masonite to support your relief map.

Salt dough is easy to make and relatively inexpensive. It can be prepared in class and used immediately or the students can make individual portions at home and bring it in an airtight plastic bag. It is quite easy to work with and will harden in one or two days. Food coloring may be added to the dough or tempera paints may be used after it has dried.

Salt Dough Recipe 1
Materials: 1¼ cups unsifted flour
1 Handi-Shake package of Carey Premium salt
2¼ tablespoons powdered alum
2 tablespoons vegetable oil
¾ cup boiling water

Mix flour, salt and alum thoroughly, add water and then oil. If color is desired, add food coloring to water prior to mixing or add powdered color to salt and flour before adding water. Knead thoroughly.

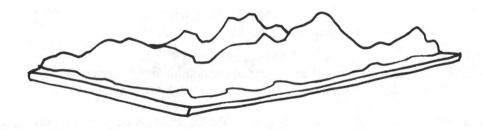

Salt Dough Recipe 2
Materials: 1 cup salt
½ cup cornstarch
¾ cup water

Mix and cook in double boiler until mixture adheres to spoon. Quickly place on aluminum foil and cool slightly. Knead until well mixed. Roll in foil or put in plastic bag.

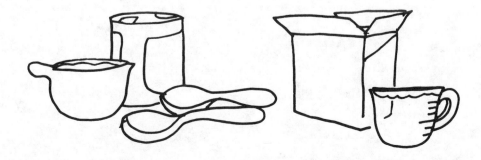

DOLPHINS

INTRODUCTION: Divide a large sheet of paper into three sections and label: Class Knowledge, What We Would Like to Know, and We Have Learned. Brainstorm any ideas the children have about dolphins—without evaluation—and list them all in the first section. Discuss facts the children are curious about and list any questions in the second section. Save the last section for a final evaluation. Display and encourage revising the information as the unit progresses.

CURRICULUM AREA/SKILLS:	ACTIVITY/TITLE	PAGE NO.
Writing outlines and paragraphs	"Whale Writing"	32-33

Using a variety of books, videotapes and films about dolphins and whales, students practice the skills—either independently or as a group—using the activity page provided.

Punctuation	"Dolphin Dialogue"	34

Following a discussion of how dolphins communicate, students practice skills by punctuating dialogue. Provide the dialogue for younger students; older children may create and punctuate their own.

Language arts; poetry	"Underwater Acrostics"	35-36

Children express themselves by writing fact or fantasy poetry. Guide younger students with the writing of a class-acrostic poem. Make a class booklet of student's individual poems.

Science	"Mammal or Fish?"	37

Students do research to discover the differences between mammals and fish and learn why dolphins and whales belong to the class of mammals.

Math	"A Whale of a Problem"	38

Provide students with various facts concerning dolphins and whales for practicing word problems orally. Students use the facts provided on the activity page to write their own word problems.

Research	"Dolphin Stumpers"	39

Students use reference materials to locate answers to questions about dolphins.

Bulletin board; art	"Dolphin Display"	40

Students create a display with construction paper replicas of the dolphin or whale they wrote about in their report. Older students may include brief descriptive summaries on a note card.

CULMINATION: Students make up a class trivia game using information from their reports to develop questions. Each student should submit 2-3 questions on an index card. Divide the class into two teams and present questions in the same manner as a spelling bee—a student who misses a question is 'out.' The team with the last remaining student 'wins.'

WHALE WRITING

The Outline

Sometimes it is helpful to gather information in outline form before writing a report. Using encyclopedias and library books, read about killer whales and complete the outline below. You may add letters for additional information if you need to.

Killer Whales

I. Description

    A. Length _____

    B. Weight _____

    C. Color _____

    D. Location _____

II. Unusual Characteristics

    A. _____

    B. _____

    C. _____

    D. _____

III. Interesting Facts

    A. _____

    B. _____

    C. _____

    D. _____

References: What sources did you use to complete this outline?

_____

_____

_____

WHALE WRITING

The Report

After completing your class outline, you are now ready to begin writing. The outline on killer whales has three main subtopics—each of which can be developed into a paragraph. Using the information under subtopic I, write the first paragraph about killer whales.

_____

_____

_____

_____

_____

_____

_____

_____

_____

_____

Now that you see the value of an outline, choose a dolphin or whale to research on your own. Write an outline and complete a report. Draw and color a picture of your dolphin or whale to accompany your report. Then, using construction paper, create a replica. Limit the finished size as follows:

> Small dolphins or whales: 10-12 in. (25-30 cm)
> Medium dolphins or whales: 12-20 in. (30-50cm)
> Large dolphins or whales: 20-30 in. (50-75cm)

DOLPHIN DIALOGUE

Trained dolphins can learn verbal directions. Although they do not have vocal cords, they do try to imitate human sounds. Dolphins have learned to respond to and even answer whistle commands.

What do you think dolphins 'talk' about?

Practice punctuating with the following punctuation marks (periods, commas, question marks, exclamation marks and quotation marks) to show conversation: . , ? ! " "

Hey Dolly Dolphin did you know Joe the killer whale is our cousin remarked Doug Dolphin

Dolly laughed Well don't invite him to lunch because you just might end up being the main course

Write a conversation between two or more dolphins. The setting can be a marine park or the open seas. Be sure to punctuate your dialogue.

_____

_____

_____

_____

_____

_____

_____

_____

_____

_____

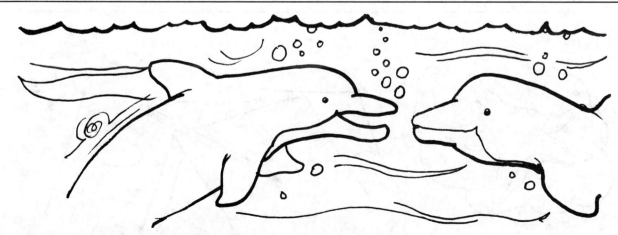

UNDERWATER ACROSTICS

Acrostic poetry does not need to rhyme. Write a topic word vertically on the paper. Use the first letter of each line to begin the first word of the line. You may write facts about your sea creature or you may write fantasy.

Starfish are sea creatures.
They are usually found attached to rocks.
All my life I have looked for a starfish.
Reading about starfish is very interesting.
Few people are lucky enough to see a real starfish.
I enjoy learning about sea creatures.
See how well I write acrostic poetry.
Hawaii would be a good place to study sealife.

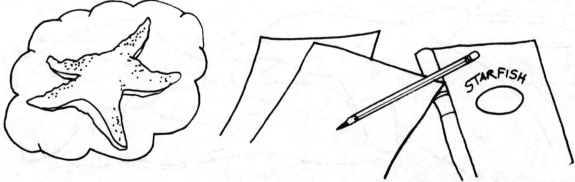

Living Things © THE MONKEY SISTERS, INC.

Dolphins and Whales

Class Poetry Book

by:

Student

Title of Poem

_____   _____

_____   _____

_____   _____

_____   _____

_____   _____

_____   _____

_____   _____

_____   _____

_____   _____

_____   _____

_____   _____

_____   _____

_____   _____

_____   _____

_____   _____

Teacher _____   **Date:** _____

"MAMMAL OR FISH?"

Do you know what the largest mammal in the world is? You may be surprised to find that it is the blue whale.

Some people consider dolphins and whales to be fish because they live in the water, but actually they are mammals. Do some research about fish and mammals and complete the activities below.

A. List the characteristics common to all mammals.

    1. _____

    2. _____

    3. _____

    4. _____

    5. _____

B. List the characteristics common to all fish.

    1. _____

    2. _____

    3. _____

    4. _____

    5. _____

C. Tell about mammals—other than dolphins and whales—that live in the water.

_____

_____

_____

_____

Living Things © THE MONKEY SISTERS, INC.

A "WHALE" OF A PROBLEM

Name _____

Listed below are facts about dolphins and whales. Make up a story problem to accompany each fact. You may use addition, subtraction, multiplication or division. When you are finished, show how to work the story problem.

Example: A bottle-nosed dolphin weighs about 400 pounds.

A tank at Sea World holds five dolphins. If each dolphin weighs 400 pounds, what would the five dolphins weigh all together?

Answer: 400   or   400 + 400 + 400 + 400 + 400 = 2,000 pounds
         ×5
      2,000 pounds

1. Killer whales can be as long as 30 feet.

    _____

    _____

    _____

    _____

2. Dolphins can swim at speeds of 25 miles per hour.

    _____

    _____

    _____

    _____

3. Some dolphins can be trained to leap 20 feet out of the
    water.

    _____

    _____

    _____

    _____

DOLPHIN STUMPERS

1. How do dolphins or porpoises locate their food and what does their main diet consist of?

_____

_____

_____

2. How does a dolphin hear?

_____

_____

_____

3. Why would it be incorrect to speak of dolphins as fish?

_____

_____

_____

4. What are young dolphins called?

_____

_____

_____

5. How do dolphins and whales differ from most mammals?

_____

_____

_____

6. What is the function of the blow hole?

_____

_____

_____

DOLPHIN DISPLAY

Students create a sealife mural display with construction paper dolphins. Older students may include brief descriptive summaries on a note card about the dolphin they researched for their report. Use a blue background, netting and other realia to create a realistic effect.

Wildflowers

INTRODUCTION: Prior to beginning this unit, you may want to contact the *National Wildflower Research Center, 2600 FM 973 North, Austin, Texas 78725, 512/929-3600* for available information and brochures. This center was founded by former First Lady, Lady Bird Johnson.

Working in small groups, students brainstorm the name of a flower for each letter of the alphabet. Discuss the wide variety of flowers and emphasize that a *wildflower* is one that grows in its natural environment. Discuss various natural environments.

Name That Flower

Choose a state that has a wildflower for its state flower.

Name of flower: _____

State it represents: _____

Three facts about the flower: Illustration or photograph of wildflower

1. _____
   _____
   _____
   _____

2. _____
   _____
   _____
   _____

3. _____
   _____
   _____
   _____

Plan a Botanical Garden

Use graph paper to design a landscape plan for a wildflower botanical garden. Plan an area of 100 feet x 35 feet. Draw a rectangle on the graph paper, to scale, with these dimensions.

Include the following accents in your wildflower garden display:
• an information center
• 3 wooden benches
• a foot bridge
• a pond
• flagstone paths to connect the various wildflower displays

Select a season and plan your garden for this season. Balance your garden by providing wildflowers in a variety of heights and colors. Illustrate showing areas of color and label each section with the name of the wildflower.

You will need to use resource books to find information about spring, summer and autumn blooms. Be sure to think about the type of growing conditions the wildflowers will be needing.

Guide questions to ask yourself:

1. What are some examples of spring wildflowers in this region?

2. Where might wildflowers be found growing in this region?

Ask these same questions of the summer and autumn seasons. This will help you in looking for the information you need to plan your wonderful, wildflower garden.

Living Things © THE MONKEY SISTERS, INC.

Flower Facts

The most important part of a plant which bears flowers, is the flower itself. The flower produces the fruit and, of course, the fruit is the 'factory' in which the seed is developed. In order to reproduce itself, the plant must have the flower.

Use resource/reference books to find information and diagrams of the parts of a flower. Write a short description of the role each part of the flower plays in the growth process. Use the magnifying glass to find each part on a real flower. Carefully open the ovary at the bottom of the pistil. Find the ovules. Draw an illustration of the flower you studied and label the four basic parts.

What is the function of each of these parts?

1. the petal _____

_____

_____

2. the sepal _____

_____

_____

3. the stamen _____

_____

_____

4. the pistil _____

_____

_____

Teacher Fact Sheet

Four basic parts of the flower:
Most flowers have four sets of parts. At the center of the flower are one or more *pistils*, surrounded by a ring of stamens. Around the stamens are the *petals*, and on the outside, the *sepals*.

The job of the sepals, also called the *calyx*, is to protect the unopened bud and seeds. The *petals* shield and guard the delicate inner parts of the flower, but even more important, their beauty attracts insects to gather pollen.

Stamens are the male parts of the flower. It is in this part where the anther is found. This is the storehouse of the pollen grain.

The *pistils* are the female parts. Each pistil has three visible parts. At the base of the pistil is the ovary, a pouch storing the ovules, or future seeds. Above the ovary is the style, with the crowning top being the stigma. The stigma is the sticky knob which catches and holds the pollen.

It is the tiny seeds inside the ovary which will be fertilized by the pollen grains, thus allowing the reproduction of the plant.

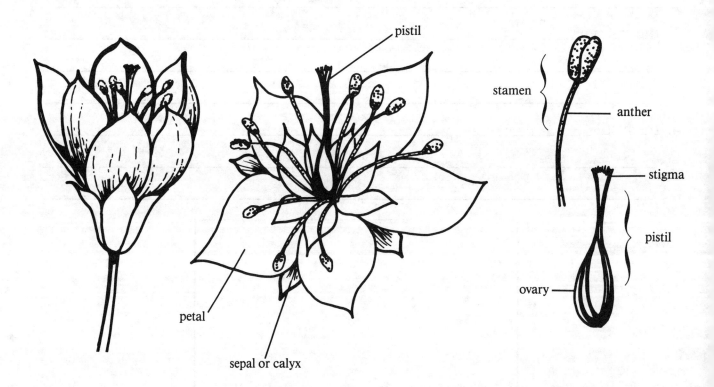

Plant and Observe

Plant a wildflower seed in one pot and a vegetable seed in another pot. Wait until a seedling appears and then record your observations on the chart below for six weeks.

wildflower

Week 1	Week 2	Week 3	Week 4	Week 5	Week 6
Drawing	Drawing	Drawing	Drawing	Drawing	Drawing
Observation:	Observation:	Observation:	Observation:	Observation:	Observation:

vegetable

Week 1	Week 2	Week 3	Week 4	Week 5	Week 6
Drawing	Drawing	Drawing	Drawing	Drawing	Drawing
Observation:	Observation:	Observation:	Observation:	Observation:	Observation:

Describe some of the similarities and differences in the vegetable and wildflower. Identify the vegetable and wildflower you studied.

Wildflower: _____   Vegetable: _____

How To Make Dried Flowers

Materials: a shoebox lined with waxed paper
1½ cups cornmeal
1½ cups 20 Mule Team Borax
3-4 tablespoons salt
florist tape
florist wire

Mix all the ingredients well and pour 1-1¼ inches of the mixture into the bottom of the lined shoebox.

Cut the stem of a fresh wildflower to approximately 1-inch in length. Push a piece of wire of the desired final length through the stem and into the flower. This will give the stem support during the drying process.

Burrow the flower, face down, into the dry mixture and pour in more to cover the bloom. Place the box in a cool, dry place for 2-3 weeks.

Remove the flowers. Shake off any residue. Twist florist tape around the wire to make strong and attractive stems on the dried flowers.

The mixture can be reused by drying it out in a warm oven and allowing it to cool prior to use.

Wild, Wildflower Bookmarks

Bookmarks, in a variety of sizes, can be made as gifts, as reading rewards for the school library, or simply as special memories of the unit of study.

Students at all levels will enjoy illustrating the wildflower of their choice with crayons or markers, colored construction paper, tissue paper, or even bright fabrics. The use of foil paper, ribbon, yarn and a pinking shears will add flair to the finished bookmark.

Provide the students with patterns on which to build their artistic work. *Require that the bookmarks be informative of the wildflower chosen by including pertinent information such as the name (both common and Latin), the growing area, color, etc.*

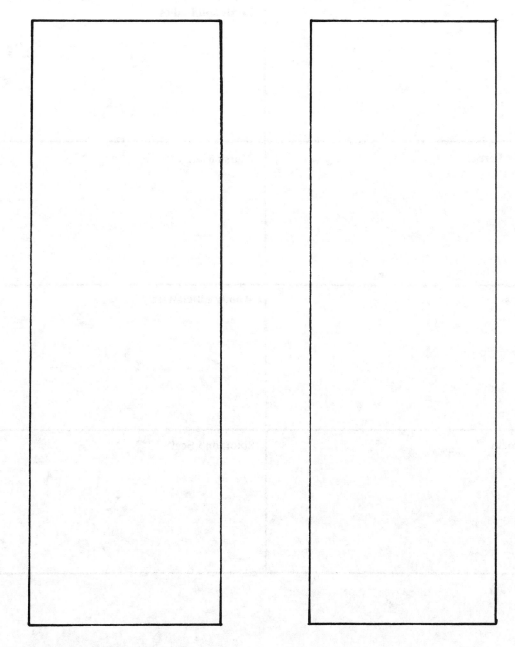

Beware! Beware!

Study wildflowers to find information about the poisonous varieties. Record information about the following flowering and berry-producing plants. Write a description of the plant, tell where it may be found, and illustrate it.

The Deadly Nightshade	**Foxglove**
Ivy Berries	**Lords and Ladies**
Honeysuckle Berries	**Marsh Marigold**
Holly Berries	**Woody Bittersweet**
Autumn Crocus	**Solomon's Seal**

Wildflower Stumpers

1. List three unusual wildflowers and write a short description of each.

_____

_____

_____

_____

_____

_____

2. Wildflowers grow in seven major different environments. Name three flowers that may be found in each of the following environments:

Arctic tundra _____

Woodlands and forests _____

Prairies and plains _____

Chaparrals _____

Alpine tundra _____

Desert _____

Tropical and sub-tropical regions _____

3. Explain the following terms:

annual _____

biennials _____

perennials _____

4. Pretend you are asked to plant a garden in your area that will include a variety of annuals, biennials and perennials. List three flowers you will plant and when you will plant them.

Annuals:	**Biennials:**	**Perennials:**

Date:_____ Date:_____ Date:_____

Trees

INTRODUCTION: Read *The Giving Tree,* by Shel Silverstein, to the class and brainstorm the uses of a tree. Display the list of ideas in the classroom. *The Giving Tree* is more than a story about a boy and a tree. In his story, Silverstein, depicts the gifts of loving and giving. Have the students recall the events of the story in sequential order.

CULMINATION: Plan an Ecology Awareness Day. Have students present information on conservation, camping safety, safety procedures when lost, prevention of damage to forested areas, etc. Display forest fire prevention posters, conservation posters, etc. Invite resource speakers—forest rangers, search and rescue teams, fire fighters—to visit your class and share with the class.

Trees

Rate your knowledge of terms related to the study of trees.

    +   I know the meaning for sure.

    ✔   I have heard this word before, but I'm not sure of the full meaning.

    ●   I have no idea what this means.

1. vegetation _____
2. tundra _____
3. temperature _____
4. forest _____
5. soil _____
6. pesticide _____
7. habitat _____
8. National Park or Forest System _____
9. needles _____
10. ecosystem _____
11. hardwood _____
12. softwood _____
13. evergreen _____

14. coniferous _____
15. deciduous _____
16. erosion _____
17. decomposition _____
18. debris _____
19. cultivation _____
20. conservation _____
21. climate _____
22. photosynthesis _____
23. broadleaf _____
24. chlorophyll _____
25. food chain _____

Why Are Trees Important?

Write the following species of trees on individual index cards and allow the students to draw one as a special topic of study.

maple	pine	fern	saguaro cactus
cypress	birch	cottonwood	dogwood
fir	elm	chestnut	magnolia
kukui oak	palm	pecan	spruce
pinon	redbud	redwood	blue spruce
tulip tree	beech	pawpaw	cherry
evergreen	locust	apple	plum
lemon	mango	peach	coffee
almond	walnut	coconut	clove
cork	kola nut	cinnamon	
holly	teak	eucalyptus	

Using the encyclopedia and a variety of reference books, students should collect important facts and perceptions describing each tree.

Share the predictable pattern of the book, *The Important Book,* by Margaret Wise Brown. Stress the development of the important characteristics of a topic. Model the pattern of the book with the class, writing a description of a particular tree.

The Apple Tree

The important thing about an apple tree is that it gives us tasty fruit.

- It shades a summer hammock,
- It blossoms in the spring,
- It safely hides a mother robin's nest . . .

But, the important thing about an apple tree is that it gives us tasty fruit.

Students may publish a class book which serves the purpose of defining the important characteristics of a variety of trees. This collective piece of prose may be titled *The Important Book of Trees.*

My Family Tree

Every family has a story. Find out as much as you can about your family. Talk to your parents and grandparents to find out more about their lives. The following questions might help when you are visiting and interviewing with different family members. Write some of your own interview questions. Take notes as you are visiting so that you will remember the information.

Interview Questions

1. What was it like when you were in grade school?

   _____

2. Where did you live when you were a child?

   _____

3. What were some things you did for entertainment as you were growing up? What were your favorite games or toys?

   _____

4. What do you think is the most significant invention that has occurred in your lifetime?

   _____

5. _____

   _____

6. _____

   _____

7. _____

   _____

Organize your notes and write your rough draft. You may want to divide your paper into sub-topics such as great grandparents, grandparents, and parents. At the end of your paper, tell about yourself. After you have written your rough draft, revise and edit it for final publication. Include illustrations or photographs with the paper you hand in.

Save Our Trees!

Each year man's impact on nature results in the loss of forested land. Brainstorm with the class the reasons for human-caused destruction of forests. Using the news media, share stories of fires, logging, mining, farming and ranching as they impact on the nation's forests.

Pinpoint the location of forests in trouble. Information can be collected from forestry services, conservation organizations, etc. Apply map and globe skills to locate these forests.

Have students report on current events, write letters to political figures, brainstorm solutions, and even prepare advertising to inform the public of the impact of deforestation on the balance of nature.

Writing the News

Teacher information: Draw an inverted triangle on the board. This is the format every news story follows and it has important functions. (1) any story may be cut to make way for more news along any line of the triangle, (2) the style allows the reader to read for the facts quickly without reading the entire article.

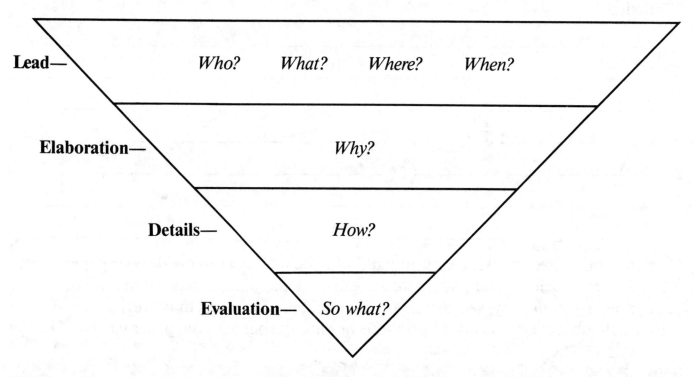

Have students practice identifying the parts of the triangle using real news articles cut from the newspaper. Students can research existing or past forest destruction in the area to incorporate the 5W and 1H of good news reporting. Dependent upon abilities, students can complete the different levels of the inverted triangle in their own writing.

Tree Stumpers

1. List 10 products that are produced from trees.

_____ _____

_____ _____

_____ _____

_____ _____

_____ _____

2. How are trees helpful in conservation?

_____

_____

_____

3. Trees can be divided into two main groups—deciduous and conifer. Name three trees in each group common to your area.

_____

_____

_____

4. How does a tree differ from a plant?

_____

_____

_____

5. Explain the term *photosynthesis*.

_____

_____

_____

6. What is your state tree? Why do you think it was chosen to be your state tree?

_____

_____

_____

Thinking About Trees

Mental Set Activities for Creative Thinking

The following activities may be used as quick-thinking exercises, as stimulus to creative writing ideas, an introduction to an academic unit of study, or even as research areas.

1. Have small groups of children brainstorm the variety of occurrences of the word 'trees' or related words, in the titles or books or names of songs.

2. Make a list of the word 'tree' as it appears in phrases: *"up a tree," "shoe tree," "family tree,"* etc.

3. Have students research famous forests in literature: Snow White, Hansel and Gretel, Sherwood Forest, etc.

4. List street names and city names referring to 'tree' words such as Oak Street, Maple Street, etc. Use this activity to reinforce local area map skills.

5. Brainstorm the variety of products yielded from trees: make it wide open in scope or limit it to, perhaps, the classroom.

6. List animals who make their homes in the forest.

7. List the states or provinces that are most highly forested.

8. Brainstorm a list of jobs created by the forestry industry.

9. Brainstorm the dangers—natural or manmade—to our forests. (fire, pollution, erosion)

Forest Facts

The Mature Forest: The established, or mature forest, has several layers of vegetation, each providing a usable habitat for a different type of animal.

Canopy—the tallest trees: There are two kinds of canopies: *the closed canopy*—where the trees grow very close together allowing little sunlight to the forest below, and *the open canopy*—which has trees much more widely spread. In the open canopy, sunlight to the forest is plentiful. Forests are named for the species of tree which grows most predominantly. For example, there are oak forests, pine forests, sugar maple forests, etc. The kind of tree will determine, in part, the canopy.

Understory: The *understory* is made up of either younger trees of the same variety as the canopy, or simply low-growing trees. The amount of understory growth is regulated by the density of the canopy.

Shrub Layer: This vegetation is mostly woody plants with several stems, rarely growing taller than 6-7 feet.

Herb Layer: Here we find the green plants with soft stems. The amount of vegetation at this layer is dependent upon the location of the forest, the soil, and the moisture.

Forest Floor: This layer is the "litter bag" of the forest! All the natural droppings of plant and animal life cycle through a process of decomposition, to provide the fertilizer for forest growth.

Discuss with students the make-up of a mature forest; sharing photographs and slides of forests. Provide a schema of forest life. Discuss the types of animals that may be found at each layer.

Older students, individually or in small groups, may research a particular kind of forest (maple, pine, etc.) and describe the vegetation and animal life at each layer of the forest. Younger students may work together on a class mural illustrating a mature forest using trees common to the area.

Make a Travel Brochure

Students should each choose a national park or forest and prepare a travel brochure to guide tourists through a visit. Students may wish to write to the National Forest Service for factual information to include along with their own ideas.

Collect a variety of travel brochures from local travel agencies to share ideas of format and style.

A guideline of information to be included might be:
1) a map of the park or forest, including its location in the nation
2) a slogan
3) photographs and captions of special attraction
4) regulations and fees
5) address and phone numbers for more information

The children might also enjoy showing the locations of their parks and forests on a large map in the classroom or library.